Match the coins

COINS

9p

6p

7p

8p

Problem solving

Colour 3 coins to buy a  .

Put out coins.

Draw the coins.

8p

4p

6p

Use 3 coins.

Problem solving

9p

Ten pence

**Put out coins.
Make each set worth**

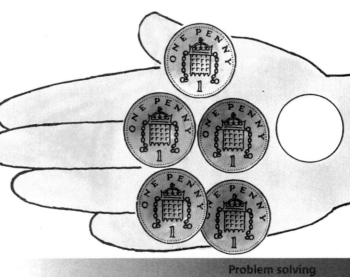

Colour coins to make 10p.

Buying things

Tom spends 10p altogether.
Write the price of the boat.

3p

2p

Lili spends 10p.
She buys two things.
Colour their labels.

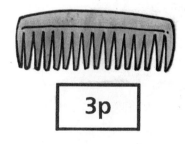

3p

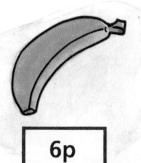

6p

4p

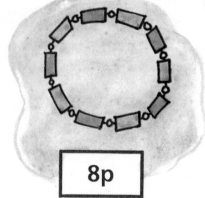

8p

7p

Buying stickers

Use coins. Put out the change.

R6

2p

Change from 5p

1p

Change from 5p

7p

Change from 10p

4p

Change from 10p

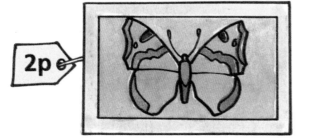

2p

Change from 10p

R7,8

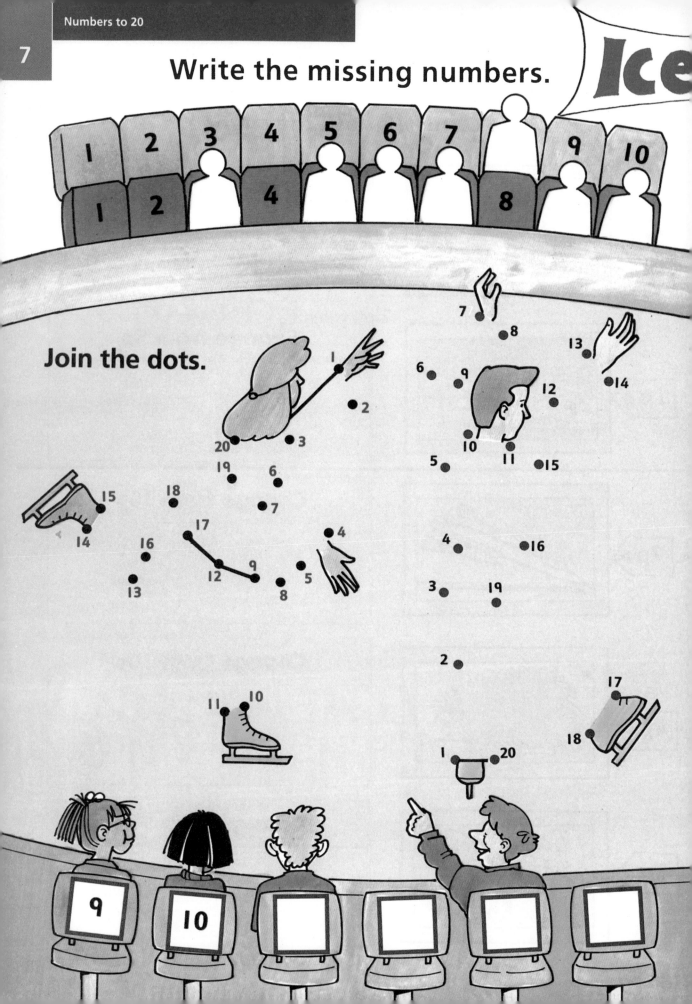

show

Write the number

after 13

after 19

after 17

before 17

before 11

before 20

15

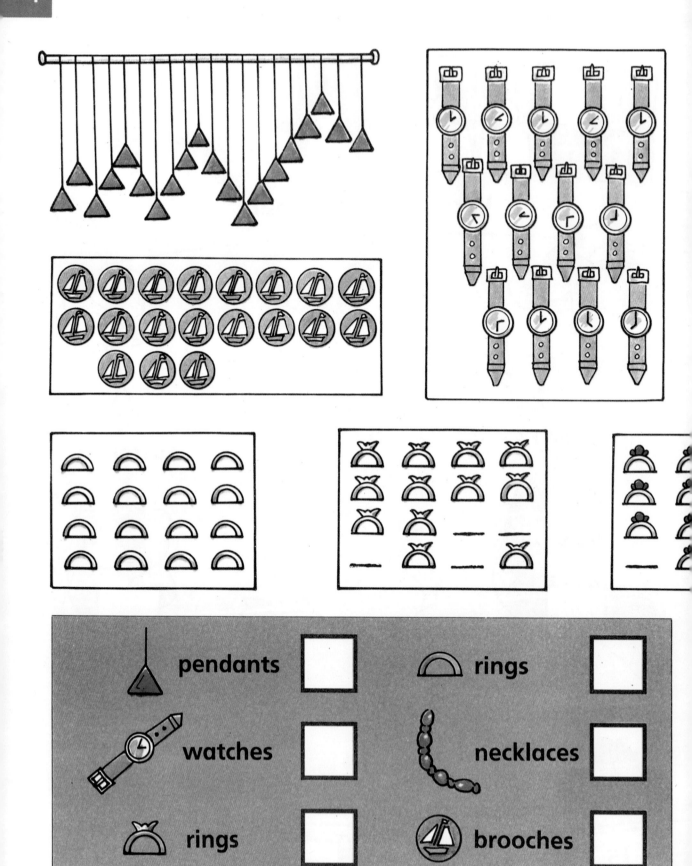

pendants			rings	
watches			necklaces	
rings			brooches	

Jewellery shop

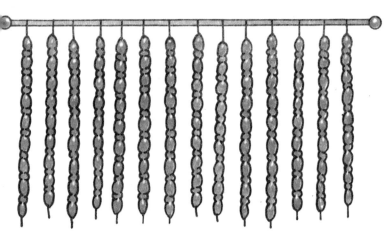

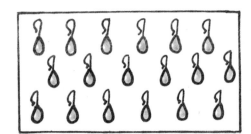

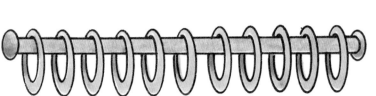

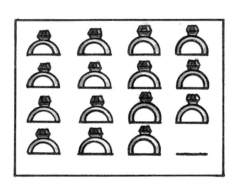

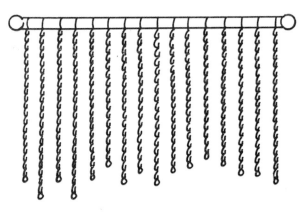

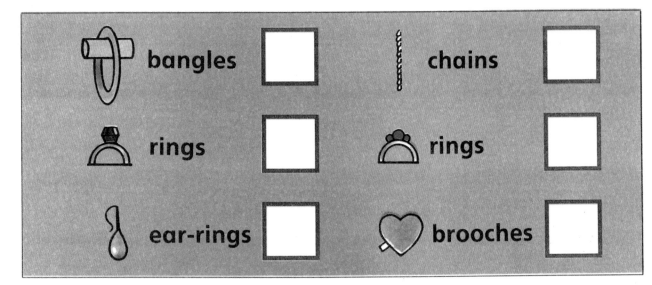

bangles ☐

chains ☐

rings ☐

rings ☐

ear-rings ☐

brooches ☐

Write the numbers.

Colour twenty red, twelve blue, thirteen yellow and

Use a calculator to show these numbers.
Write the numbers.

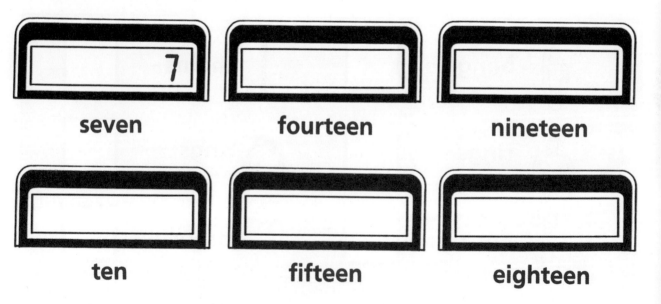

seven   fourteen   nineteen

ten   fifteen   eighteen

ames

sixteen   seventeen   eighteen   nineteen   twenty

seventeen green.

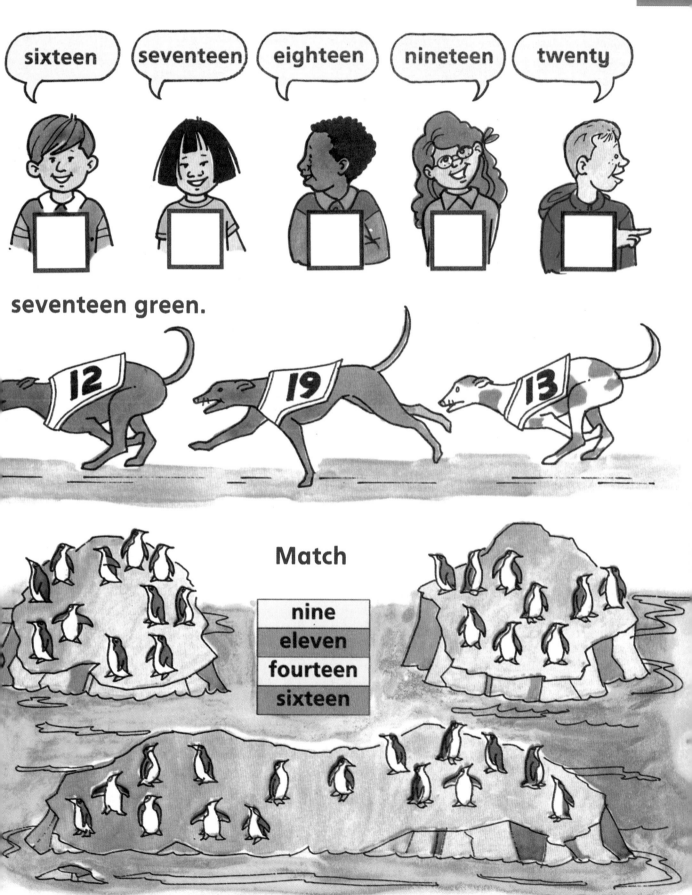

Match

| nine |
| eleven |
| fourteen |
| sixteen |

The sunflower

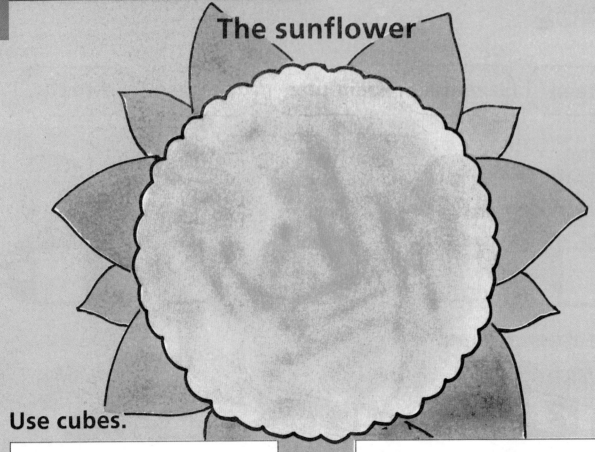

Use cubes.

Count out 13.

Put 10 on the .

13 = 10 and 3

Count out 19.

Put 10 on the .

19 = 10 and ___

Count out 15.

Put 10 on the .

15 = 10 and ___

Count out 18.

Put 10 on the .

18 = 10 and ___

Count out 16.

Put 10 on the .

16 = ___ and ___

Count out 12.

Put 10 on the .

12 = ___ and ___

The beanstalk

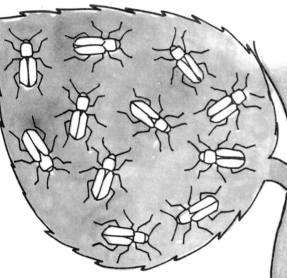

How many? ____
Colour 10 red.

11 = 10 + ___

How many? ____
Colour 10 yellow.

14 = 10 + ___

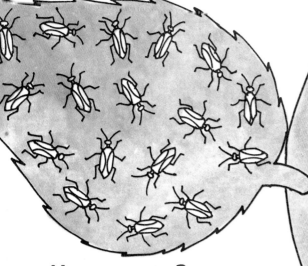

How many? ____
Colour 10 blue.

17 = ___ + ___

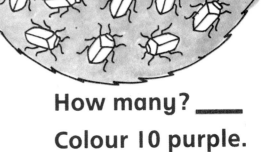

How many? ____
Colour 10 purple.

15 = ___ + ___

19 = ___ + ___

12 = ___ + ___

16 = ___ + ___

The garden centre

10 plants

10 canes

10 + ___

How many altogether?

10 + ___

How many altogether?

10 roses

10 pots

10 + ___

How many altogether?

10 + ___

How many altogether?

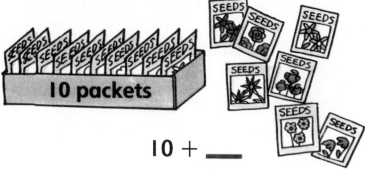

10 packets

10 bulbs

10 + ___

How many altogether?

10 + ___

How many altogether?

Loading bricks

tens

Count out 13. Make a ten.

$13 = \underline{1}$ ten $+ \underline{}$ units

$15 = \underline{}$ ten $+ \underline{}$ units

$18 = \underline{}$ ten $+ \underline{}$ units

$14 = \underline{}$ ten $+ \underline{}$ units

$17 = \underline{}$ ten $+ \underline{}$ units

$19 = \underline{}$ ten $+ \underline{}$ units

$11 = \underline{}$ ten $+ \underline{}$ unit

$16 = \underline{}$ ten $+ \underline{}$ units

$12 = \underline{}$ ten $+ \underline{}$ units

$20 = \underline{}$ tens $+ \underline{}$ units

units

More bricks

tens

units

Put out 1 ten and 5 units.

How many
cubes altogether? ☐

1 ten + 5 units = ☐

1 ten + 2 units = ☐

1 ten + 7 units = ☐

1 ten + 4 units = ☐

1 ten + 1 unit = ☐

1 ten + 6 units = ☐

2 tens + 0 units = ☐

Cranes

Colour the boxes to match the cranes.

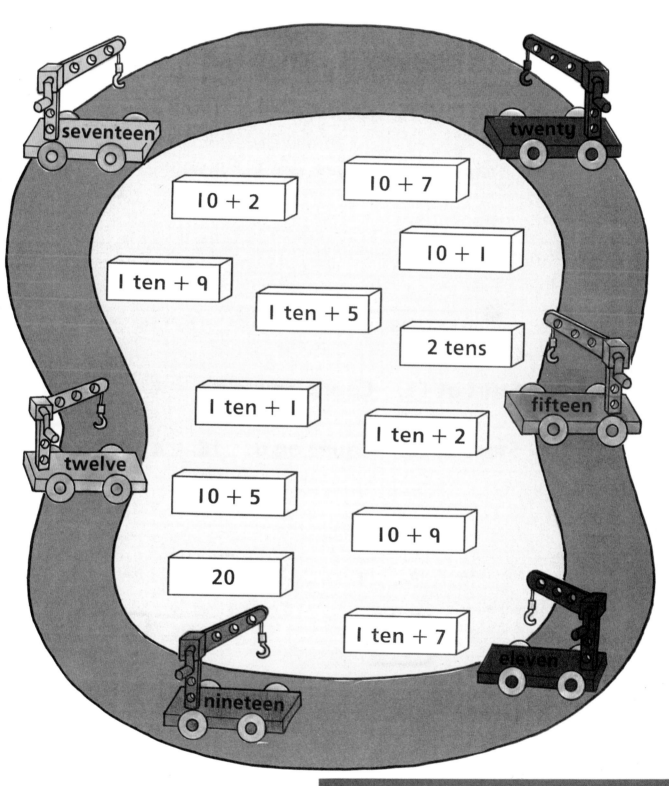

Bunny hops

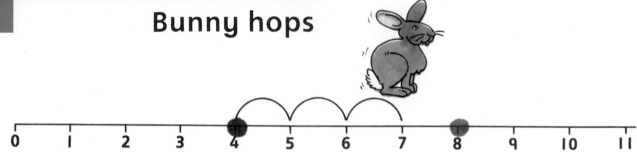

Start at 4.   Count on 3. $4 + 3 =$ ☐

Start at 8.   Count on 3. $8 + 3 =$ ☐

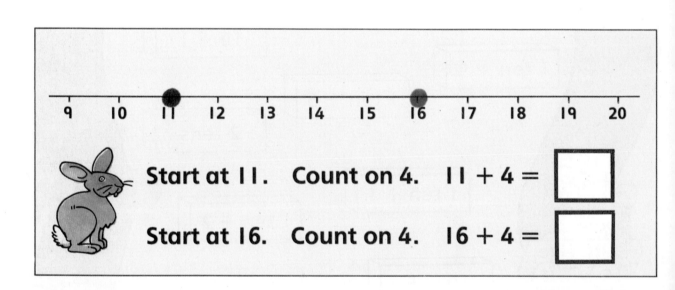

Start at 11.   Count on 4. $11 + 4 =$ ☐

Start at 16.   Count on 4. $16 + 4 =$ ☐

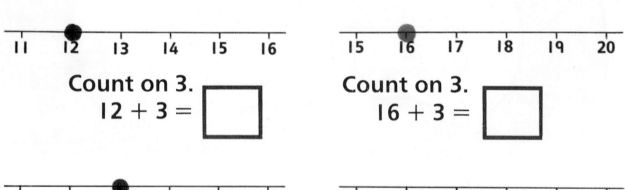

Count on 3.
$12 + 3 =$ ☐

Count on 3.
$16 + 3 =$ ☐

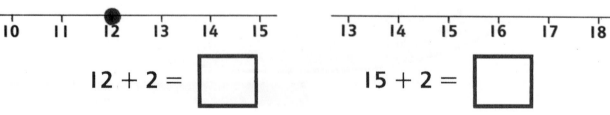

$12 + 2 =$ ☐

$15 + 2 =$ ☐

Party food

Put more cherries on the cake.

3 + ☐ = 5   3 + ☐ = 4

3 + ☐ = 6   3 + ☐ = 7

3 + ☐ = 9   3 + ☐ = 8

Draw more cakes.   Draw more cakes.

2 + ☐ = 5   5 + ☐ = 8

Draw more apples.   Draw more apples.

   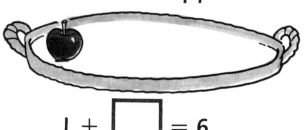

4 + ☐ = 7   1 + ☐ = 6

Boats

6 + ☐ = 10   4 + ☐ = 10

7 + ☐ = 10   3 + ☐ = 10

9 + ☐ = 10   1 + ☐ = 10

8 + ☐ = 10   2 + ☐ = 10

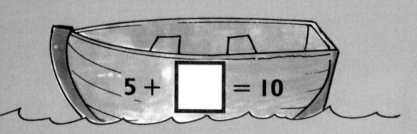

5 + ☐ = 10

6 + ☐ = 7

5 + ☐ = 9

4 + ☐ = 6

Vegetables

The difference in price is ☐ p. $6 - 4 =$

You may use coins.

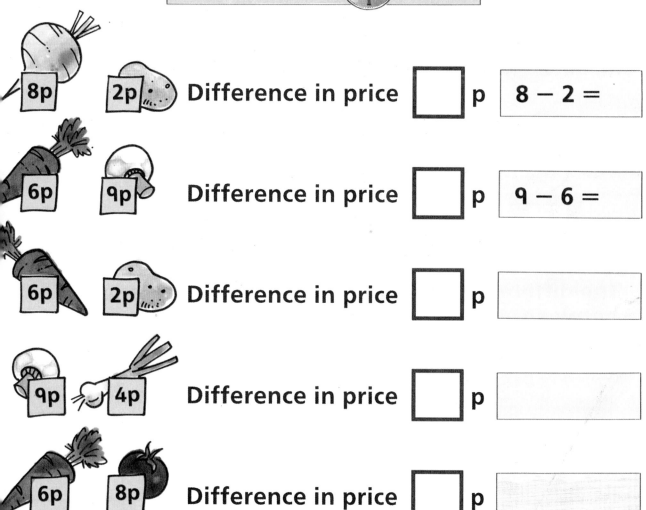

Difference in price ☐ p $8 - 2 =$

Difference in price ☐ p $9 - 6 =$

Difference in price ☐ p

Difference in price ☐ p

Difference in price ☐ p

R 10

Plants

☐ plants

☐ plants

The difference between 9 and 6 is ___ . $9 - 6 =$ ☐

☐ trees

☐ trees

The difference between 4 and 8 is ___ . $8 - 4 =$ ☐

☐ leaves   ☐ leaves

The difference between 7 and 5 is ___ .

$7 - 5 =$ ☐

The difference between 6 and 3 is ___ .

$6 - 3 =$ ☐

The difference between 2 and 9 is ___ .

$9 - 2 =$ ☐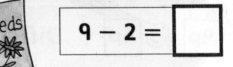

1	2	3	4	5	6	7	8	9	10	11	12	13	14	15	16	17	18	19	20	21	22	23

Heinemann is an imprint of Pearson Education Limited, a company incorporated in England and Wales, having its registered office at Edinburgh Gate, Harlow, Essex, CM20 2JE.
Registered company number: 872828
ISBN 978 0 435 03092 6 © Scottish Primary Mathematics Group 1981.
First published 1991. Revised edition 1995.   16   24
Typeset and Illustrated by Oxprint Design. Printed and bound in Malaysia (CTP-PJB)

ISBN 978-0-435030-92-6
9 780435 030926